Robert S. Frost & Deborah Baker Monday

Book 1

17 Beginning-Level Ensembles
for String Instruments

Contents

ISBN 0-8497-3427-4

kjos NEIL A. KJOS MUSIC COMPANY • San Diego, California

Using *Artistry in Ensembles*

Artistry in Ensembles is very versatile in meeting the needs of young orchestras. The folk songs, arrangements, and original music in this collection are perfect for festivals and concerts. All selections are written in a three-part format allowing for maximum sound from any size ensemble. The charts below show the assignment of parts and the possible instrument combinations.

Tempos, dynamics, and articulations have been indicated on all selections. Although some students may not be acquainted with all the terms, they are included with the hope that their use and the development of the required skills will motivate students to reach for an artistic level of performance.

Performance notes and rehearsal suggestions for each selection are included in the back of the score.

Putting the Parts Together

The melody, labeled "A," is featured in all the part books. An additional harmony or bass line is also included for each instrument: "B" in violin and viola; "C" in cello and bass.

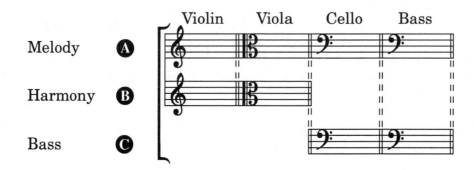

A variety of combinations will work well for classroom and performance situations. Here are some suggestions:

A	**B**	**C**
1. All (w/Piano)		
2. Violin and/or Viola	Violin and/or Viola	
3. Violin	Viola	Cello
4. Cello		Bass
5. Violin and/or Viola	Violin and/or Viola	Cello and/or Bass

Double Bass

The Double Bass book offers two fingering systems to the performer. The Low Position and Middle Position approaches as presented in *Artistry in Strings, Book 1,* have been combined into one Double Bass book for *Artistry in Ensembles, Book 1.* The first 9 pieces in this collection offer separate pages for each approach. The traditional approach (marked LP for Low Position) is shown on the left page while the Middle Position (marked MP) is featured on the right page. These two systems combine for the 2nd half of the book. Aside from some octave differences, the music is identical in both approaches and the use of either one will ensure successful performances of the selections from *Artistry in Ensembles.* On combined pages, LP fingerings appear above the staff and MP fingerings appear below. Roman numerals indicate the strings; I = G string, II = D string, III = A string, IV = E string.

For more information regarding Middle Position, please refer to *Artistry in Strings, Book 1,* by Robert S. Frost and Gerald Fischbach.

Piano

Optional easy to intermediate-level accompaniments for teachers or students with moderate keyboard skills are included in the score and in a separate book. The accompaniments feature the Violin "A" and "B" parts and the Cello "C" part above the piano grand staff.

Piano accompaniments are provided to enhance the music and assist in helping students learn the music more quickly. In general, they are reductions of the string parts and provide a strong harmonic foundation and rhythmic pulse that can strengthen rehearsal and performance. Using the piano will strengthen any of the suggested performance combinations listed on page 2 of the score.

The articulations generally match those in the string parts. However, pianists should adapt these articulations as appropriate and use pedaling as necessary. The chord symbols included above the piano part provide a harmonic reduction of the score for use by a guitarist or a pianist wishing to create his or her own accompaniment.

Percussion

Optional percussion parts are included for some selections to add color and interest in the music and to reinforce counting and improve students' sense of time and pulse. The owner of this score is authorized to duplicate and distribute pages 126–139 for classroom and performance use.

Each song includes a list of instruments that may be used when performing the percussion parts. It is not intended that all instruments be used and some instruments may be more suitable for a particular selection than others (see performance notes). The number of players and instruments will depend on individual circumstances. Other instruments can be substituted if desired and/or available. See page 125 of this manual for more information.

The symbol △126 placed next to the list of percussion instruments refers to the page on which the percussion part can be found in the back of this score.

Duplication Authorization Certificate

This certificate authorizes permission to make up to three photocopies each of the following pages from *Artistry in Ensembles, Book 1* to meet specific requirements for music festivals, contests, and competitions:

Hard Rock Highway — pages 4–9	**Ballades of the American West** — pages 56–65
Vittles Valse — pages 10–14	**The Spirit of America** — pages 66–76
Ancient Mother — pages 15–19	**Chester** — pages 77–79
Bolero — pages 20–25	**Galactic Odyssey** — pages 80–88
Pop, Popcorn! Pop! — pages 26–35	**Mattachins** — pages 89–99
Lo Yisa Goy — pages 36–40	**Engine 91** — pages 100–108
Kutsu ga Naru — papers 41–45	**Festival of Brahms** — pages 109–119
Minuet — pages 46–50	**Shuckin' the Corn** — pages 120–124
King William's March — pages 51–55	

Photocopied pages may not be sold or borrowed, and must be destroyed at the conclusion of the event.

KJOS NEIL A. KJOS MUSIC COMPANY, *Publisher* • 858-270-9800 • email@kjos.com

Percussion I: Snare Drum
Percussion II: Bass Drum
Percussion III: Suspended Cymbal

Hard Rock Highway

Deborah Baker Monday

106F

Percussion I: Tambourine, Triangle, Finger Cymbals, Suspended Cymbal, Sandpaper Blocks
Percussion II: Hand Drum, Tone Block, Wood Block, Bass Drum

Vittles Valse

Robert S. Frost

+ Left hand pizzicato. Strum across the strings.

Percussion I: Triangle
Percussion II: Large Hand Drum (with soft mallet)

Ancient Mother

**Traditional Native American
arr. Deborah Baker Monday**

Percussion I: Large Hand Drum
Percussion II: Maracas
Percussion III: Claves, Rhythm Sticks, Castanets

Bolero

Deborah Baker Monday

106F

Percussion I: Rhythm Sticks, Temple Blocks, Tone Block, Castanets
131 Percussion II: Bongo Drum, Hand Drum, Conga Drum, Tom-tom

Pop, Popcorn! Pop!

Robert S. Frost

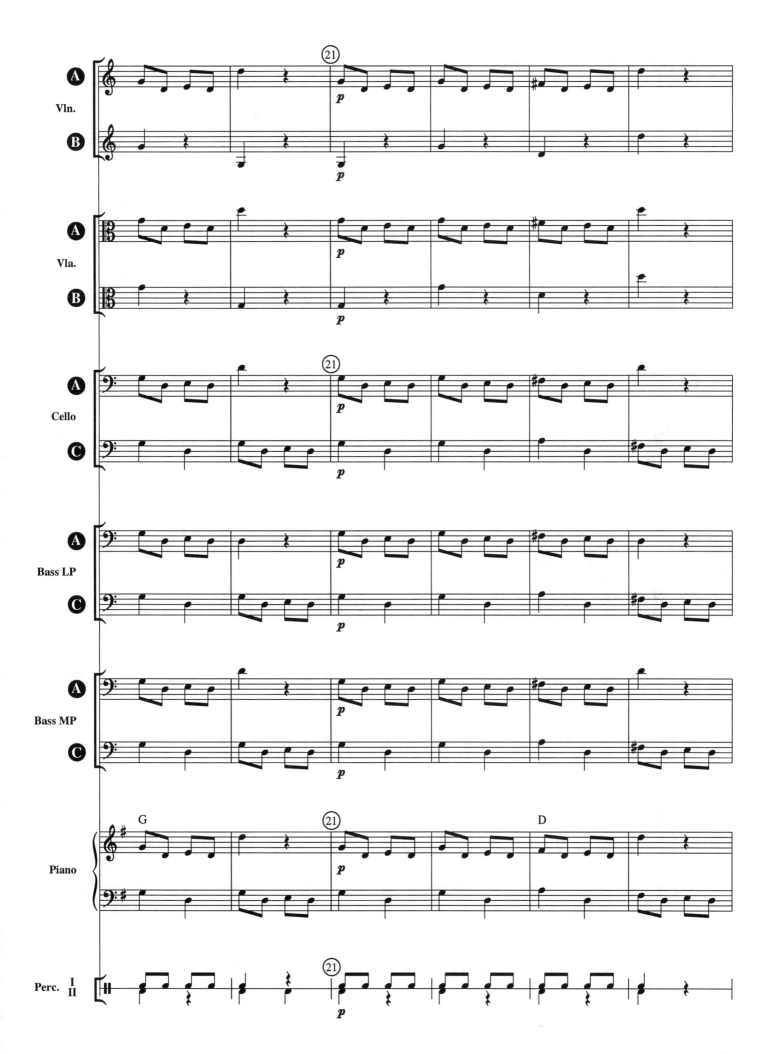

Percussion I: Tambourine

Lo Yisa Goy
(A Song of Peace)

Traditional Jewish
arr. Deborah Baker Monday

Percussion I: Suspended Cymbal, Finger Cymbals, Sandpaper Blocks, Wood Block, Jingle Stick
Percussion II: Tambourine, Triangle, Jingle Stick, Wood Block

Kutsu ga Naru
(The Sound of Shoes)

Japanese Children's Song
arr. Robert S. Frost

Minuet

Georg Philipp Telemann (1681-1767)
arr. Deborah Baker Monday

King William's March

Jeremiah Clarke (c. 1674-1707)
arr. Robert S. Frost

Ballades of the American West

American Folk Songs
arr. Robert S. Frost

"Lonesome Cowboy"

Percussion I: Snare Drum, Hand Drum
Percussion II: Tambourine, Bass Drum
Percussion III: Maracas, Shaker, Suspended Cymbal
Percussion IV: Rhythm Sticks, Claves

134

The Spirit of America
Variations on "Yankee Doodle"

Traditional
arr. Deborah Baker Monday

Chester

William Billings (1746-1800)
arr. Robert S. Frost

Percussion I: Bass Drum, Large Hand Drum
Percussion II: Suspended Cymbal
Percussion III: Triangle, Finger Cymbals, Chime Tree

136

Galactic Odyssey

Deborah Baker Monday

* Slide slowly up the string with the 1st finger.

** Play strings behind the bridge.
*** Alternate between the two notes as rapidly as possible.

✳ Slide slowly up the string with the 1st finger.

†Make nontraditional sounds on your instrument. Try tapping the body, sliding the 1st finger
  up and down the strings, bowing behind the bridge, tremolo, and "snap" pizzicato. Watch the
  conductor for the cutoff.
  Percussion and Piano: Make up your own rhythms and sound effects on your instrument. Watch
  the conductor for the cutoff.

††This measure should last 8-15 seconds.

Mattachins
(Sword Dance)

Traditional French
arr. Deborah Baker Monday

* Lower part is optional.

Percussion I: Wood Block, Tone Block, Sandpaper Blocks, Rhythm Sticks
Percussion II: Tambourine, Guiro, Tom-tom, Hand Drum

Engine 91

Robert S. Frost

Festival of Brahms

Johannes Brahms (1833-1897)
arr. Deborah Baker Monday

Shuckin' the Corn

American Folk Song
arr. Robert S. Frost

Percussion

Optional percussion parts are included for some selections to add color and interest in the music and to reinforce counting and improve students' sense of time and pulse. The owner of this score is authorized to duplicate and distribute the following 14 pages for classroom and performance use.

Each song includes a list of instruments that may be used when performing the percussion parts. It is not intended that all instruments be used and some instruments may be more suitable for a particular selection than others. The number of players and instruments will depend on individual circumstances. Other instruments can be substituted if desired and/or available. The following are the suggested percussion instruments in *Artistry in Ensembles*.

Bass Drum
Bongo Drum
Castanets
Claves
Conga Drum
Finger Cymbals
Guiro
Hand Drum (with and without a mallet)
Jingle Stick
Maracas
Rhythm Sticks
Sandpaper Blocks
Snare Drum
Suspended Cymbal (with stick)
Tambourine
Tom-tom
Tone Block
Triangle
Wood Block

Percussion I: Snare Drum
Percussion II: Bass Drum
Percussion III: Suspended Cymbal

Hard Rock Highway

Deborah Baker Monday

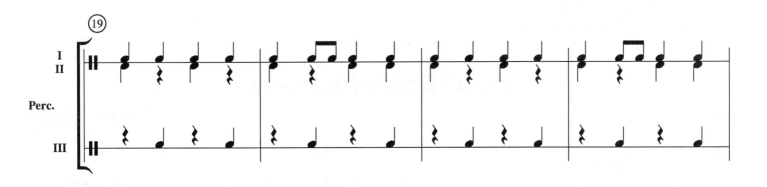

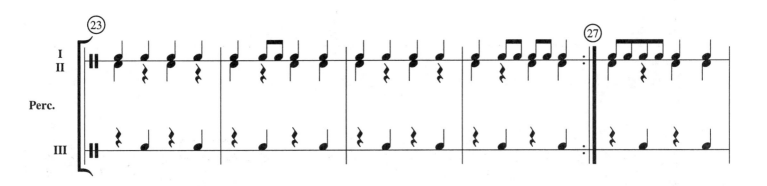

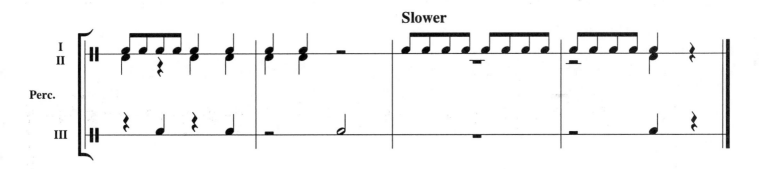

Percussion I: Tambourine, Triangle, Finger Cymbals, Suspended Cymbal, Sandpaper Blocks
Percussion II: Hand Drum, Tone Block, Wood Block, Bass Drum

Vittles Valse

Robert S. Frost

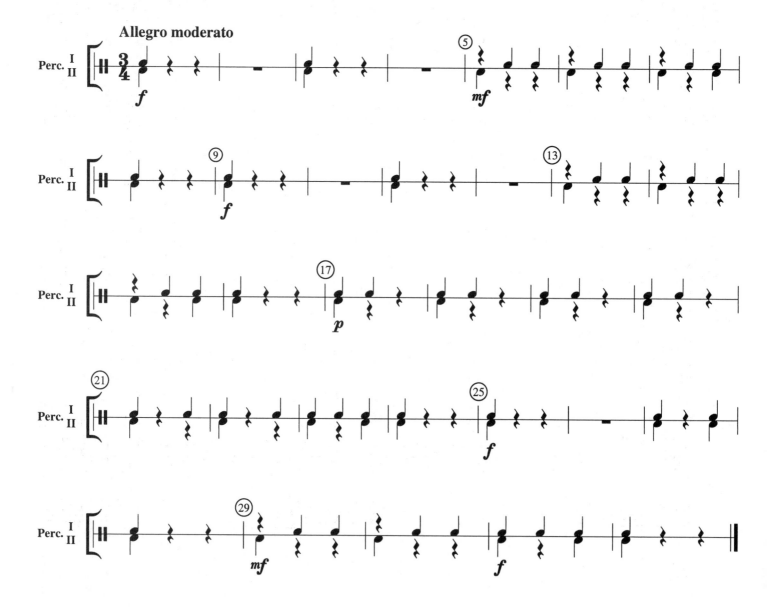

Percussion I: Triangle
Percussion II: Large Hand Drum (with soft mallet)

Ancient Mother

**Traditional Native American
arr. Deborah Baker Monday**

Percussion I: Large Hand Drum
Percussion II: Maracas
Percussion III: Claves, Rhythm Sticks, Castanets

Bolero

Deborah Baker Monday

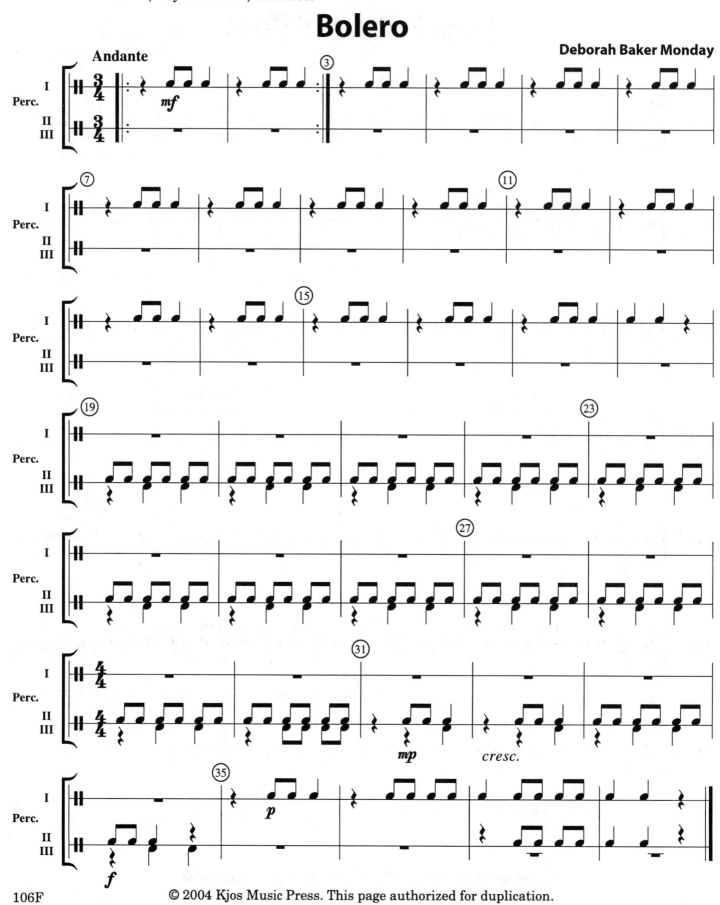

© 2004 Kjos Music Press. This page authorized for duplication.

Percussion I: Rhythm Sticks, Temple Blocks, Tone Block, Castanets
Percussion II: Bongo Drum, Hand Drum, Conga Drum, Tom-tom

Pop, Popcorn! Pop!

Robert S. Frost

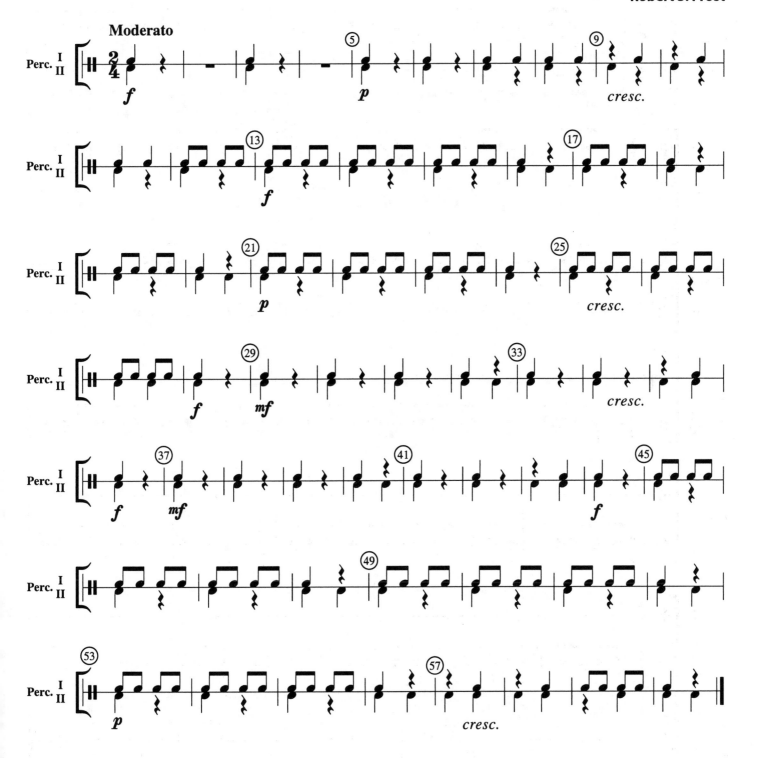

Percussion I: Tambourine

Lo Yisa Goy
(A Song of Peace)

Traditional Jewish
arr. Deborah Baker Monday

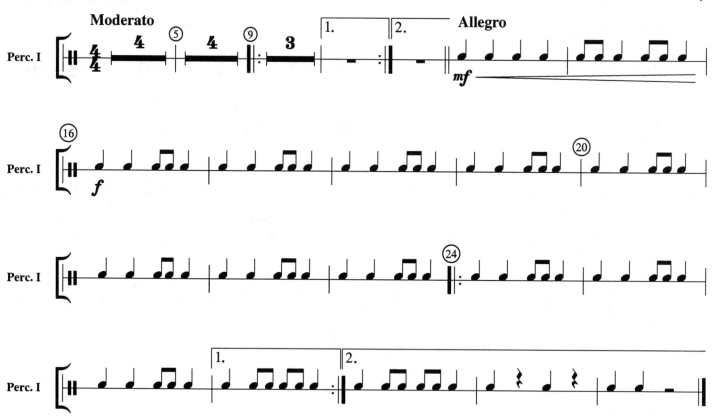

Percussion I: Suspended Cymbal, Finger Cymbals, Sandpaper Blocks, Wood Block, Jingle Stick
Percussion II: Tambourine, Triangle, Jingle Stick, Wood Block

Kutsu ga Naru
(The Sound of Shoes)

Japanese Children's Song
arr. Robert S. Frost

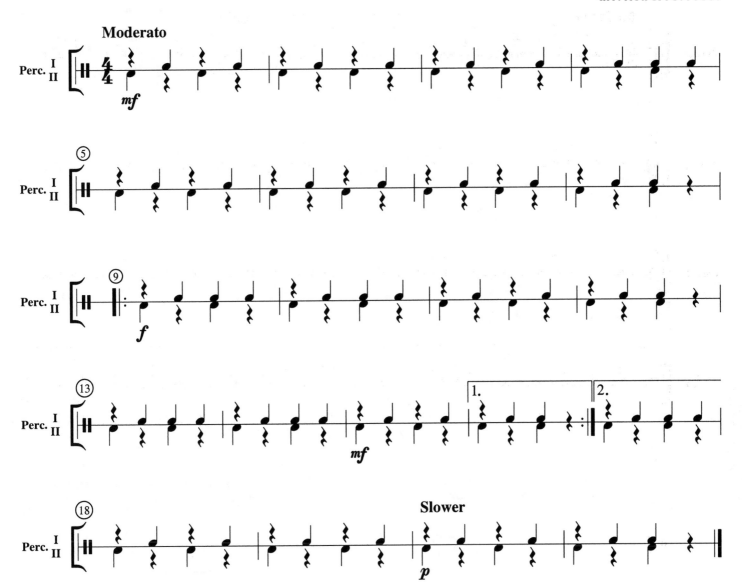

Percussion I: Snare Drum, Hand Drum
Percussion II: Tambourine, Bass Drum
Percussion III: Maracas, Shaker, Suspended Cymbal
Percussion IV: Claves, Rhythm Sticks

The Spirit of America
Variations on "Yankee Doodle"

Traditional
arr. Deborah Baker Monday

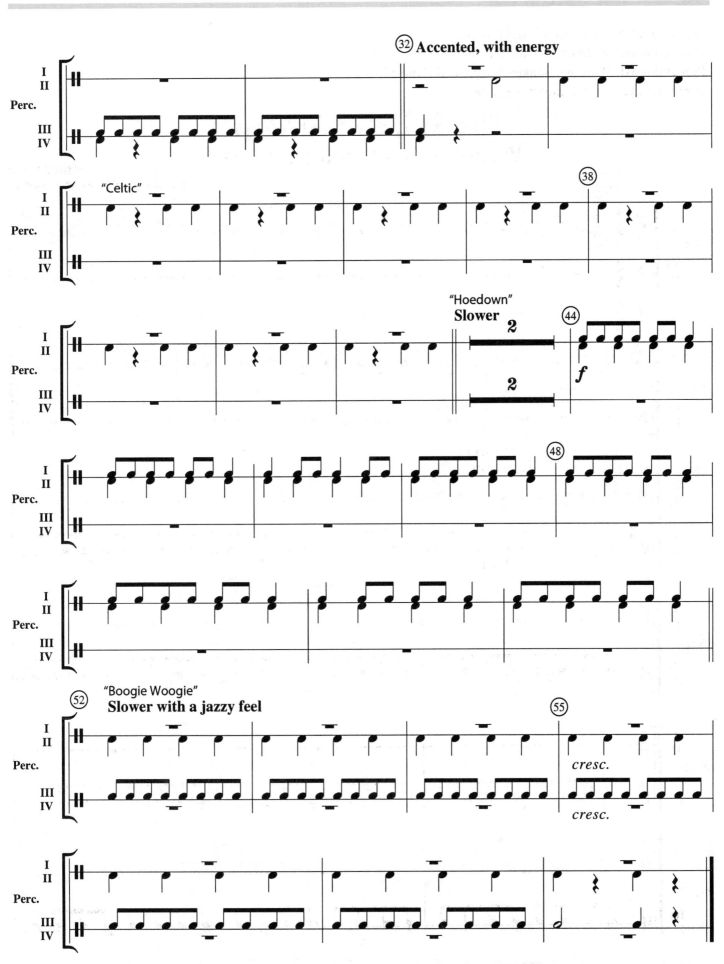

Percussion I: Bass Drum, Large Hand Drum
Percussion II: Suspended Cymbal
Percussion III: Triangle, Finger Cymbals, Chime Tree

Galactic Odyssey

Deborah Baker Monday

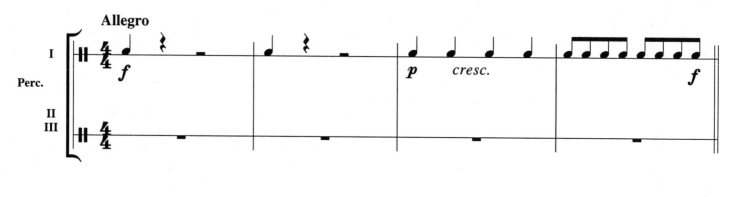

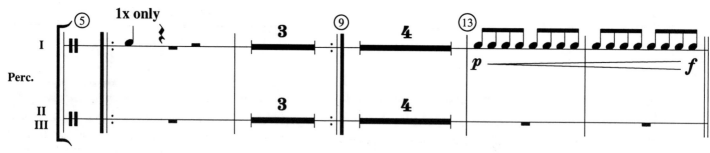

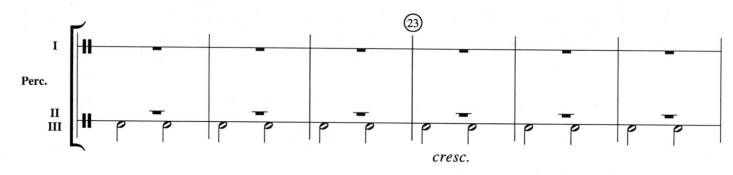

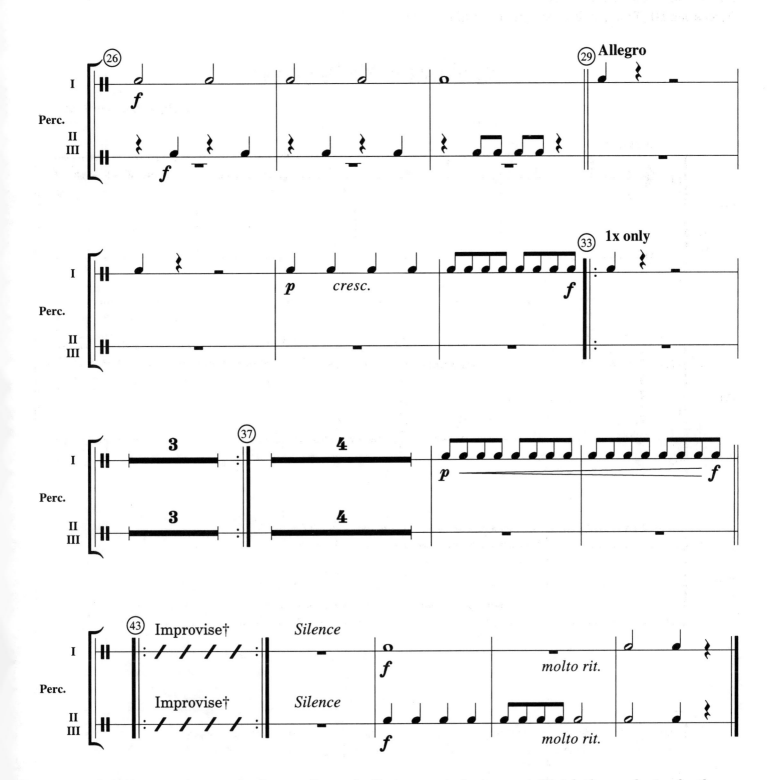

† Make up your own rhythms and sound effects on your instrument. Watch the conductor for the cutoff.

Percussion I: Wood Block, Tone Block, Sandpaper Blocks, Rhythm Sticks
Percussion II: Tambourine, Guiro, Tom-tom, Hand Drum

Engine 91

Robert S. Frost

Notes and Suggestions

Hard Rock Highway
Deborah Baker Monday

score page 4 • student book page 2

This original rock-style composition is based on the D Minor Blues chord progression. The "ad lib." section at measure 15 can be used to reinforce any of the rhythm patterns listed below. Feel free to feature students as "soloists" or feature a section of the orchestra. Repeat this section as many times as desired until everyone has had a chance to play.

1. ♩ ♫ ♫ ♩   2. ♫ ♫ ♩ ♩   3. ♩ ♩ ♫ ♫

Vittles Valse
Robert S. Frost

score page 10 • student book page 3

"Valse" is French for "waltz." Waltzes became popular ballroom dances in nineteenth-century Europe and are still popular today. The movements of the waltz are very graceful and consist of many turns or spins.

Allow students ample time to effectively strum across the strings. For the best-sounding harmonics, use fast bow strokes closer to the bridge. The piano part contains some countermelodies that will greatly enhance the performance.

Ancient Mother
Native American Song

score page 15 • student book page 4

This lullaby was often sung by mothers to their newborn babies. The words *Ancient Mother, I hear you calling/Ancient Mother, I hear your song*, reflect the common theme in Native American music of reaching out to one's ancestors.

Legato bow strokes are ideal for the calm and soothing nature of the music. Suggest that students "gently turn the corner" to change bow direction by making a figure 8. Also, emphasize the importance of keeping a steady rhythm during the pizzicato sections of the music.

Bolero
Deborah Baker Monday

score page 20 • student book page 5

A bolero is a Spanish dance in triple ($\frac{3}{4}$) meter danced by a man and a woman each with castanets. The dance consists of several sections ending with a gesture consisting of one arm arched over the head and the other crossed in front of the chest.

The contrasting section in D major at measure 19 should be made distinct by observing the bowing style. The violins and violas must have a good left hand position to achieve a difference between the high and low 2nd finger.

Pop, Popcorn! Pop!
Robert S. Frost

score page 26 • student book page 6

Many composers have written pieces using only pizzicato strings: *Pizzicato Polka* by Johann II & Josef Strauss, and the 3rd movement of *Symphony No. 4* by Peter Ilyich Tchaikovsky.

Keeping a steady beat is essential when playing pizzicato. Use firm left hand fingers to ensure a ringing tone. Incorporating the optional piano and percussion parts into your performance will enhance the playing experience!

Lo Yisa Goy (A Song of Peace)
Traditional Jewish

score page 36 • student book page 8

The lyrics to this song of peace translate as *Nation shall not lift up sword against nation; neither shall they learn war any more.*

Play the quarter notes accented and separated at the beginning. The first 8 measures work as a round with measures 9–14. In teaching part "A," it may be fun to employ the round for variety.

Kutsu ga Naru (The Sound of Shoes)
Japanese Children's Song

score page 41 • student book page 9

In this song, Japanese children pretend that the sounds their shoes make while walking through the woods belong to the animals and birds around them.

Rehearsal Suggestions: Divide the strength of the upper strings to ensure that the A and B parts are played equally strong. Delicate use of percussion will add a lot of color to this selection.

Minuet
George Philipp Telemann (1681–1767)

score page 46 • student book page 10

George Philipp Telemann was the most famous composer of his day. He wrote countless pieces for the harpsichord, including this minuet.

Knowing the Baroque style of bowing is an essential element of string playing. Longer note values (quarters) should be played with a separated style while shorter note values (eighths) should be played smooth and connected.

King William's March
Jeremiah Clarke (c. 1674–1707)

score page 51 • student book page 11

Jeremiah Clarke served as choir master and organist of St. Paul's Cathedral in London. He wrote this entrance march for King William III of Great Britain.

Review the bowing suggestions for the Baroque style given for "Minuet." A firm martelé stroke in the middle of the bow will produce the desired march-like quality. Adhering to the printed dynamics will breathe life into the repeated phrases.

Ballades of the American West
American Folk Songs

score page 56 • student book page 12

The cowboys of the American West were a strong and hardy group, but they often longed for the day when they would see their loved ones again. The most popular songs of the cowboy era reflect this longing in the stories they tell.

These songs are wonderful for legato bowing and provide many opportunities for phrasing and freedom with dynamics. When the strength and number of players permit, add cello and/or viola players on the melody (A Part).

The Spirit of America (Variations on "Yankee Doodle")
Traditional

score page 66 • student book page 14

"Yankee Doodle" became popular in colonial America in the 1750s but its origin dates back one hundred years in Europe. During the American Revolutionary War, the British mocked the Americans by singing their own version of "Yankee Doodle." The Americans made it their battle song by creating new words. The song was played when the British surrendered in 1781.

The styles change frequently from variation to variation. Rehearse the changes often so that students feel secure with the new style. Careful attention to the tempos, articulations and dynamics will help in playing in the proper style.

If possible, specify that Percussion II play Tambourine from measure 32 to 41 and Bass Drum from 44 to the end, and that Percussion III play Maracas from measure 18 to 32 and Suspended Cymbal from measure 52 to the end.

Chester

William Billings (1746–1800)

score page 77 • student page 16

"Chester" was the first internationally famous song written by an American-born composer. Like "Yankee Doodle," "Chester" was sung by the troops during many battles of the American Revolution. Because of the hymn-like quality of "Chester," good intonation can be encouraged and developed. Sustained bow control on the whole notes will require added attention.

Galactic Odyssey

Deborah Baker Monday

score page 80 • student page 16

"Galactic Odyssey" uses many nontraditional methods of playing the instrument to create different sounds! Acquaint students with the special effects required in measures 15–28 and other similar places. Brief explanations are provided in the student books, however, some extra guidance might be beneficial. At measure 43, be sure that the production of the nontradtional sounds won't damage the instrument. Students will enjoy discovering many different musical sounds for this selection.

Mattachins (Sword Dance)

Traditional French

score page 89 • student book page 18

This sixteenth-century dance involves a mock combat between teams of men. It is one of the few dances that was theatrical in nature, rather than social. The melody of "Mattachins" was first printed in 1588 in Orchesésographie by Thoinot Arbeau. This simple tune became an exciting dance when the sword clashes and foot stamps were added.

The slur followed by two up bows is very logical for this piece. If the students have learned spiccato, they should be encouraged to bounce the double up bows.

Engine 91

Robert S. Frost

score page 100 • student book page 20

The repeated eighth notes in "Engine 91" make this piece almost sound like a machine. A steady tempo will help create this effect. The spiccato bow stroke will be easier once a lively tempo is achieved. Crisp martelé strokes on the quarter notes will also help the momentum. Encourage strong pick-up bows on the half notes leading into measure 23 and the *D.C.*

Festival of Brahms

Johannes Brahms (1833–1897)

score page 109 • student book page 22

This piece combines themes from Brahms's *Academic Festival Overture* and the final movement of *Symphony No. 1*. Brahms wrote *Academic Festival Overture* in 1880 for the University of Breslau to thank them for giving him an honorary degree. *Symphony No. 1* was completeted in 1876 after 21 years of writing!

A rich and full sound is representative of Brahms's style and can be created with long bow strokes utilizing the whole bow. However, spiccato is required from measure 9 to 41. Notes not marked with staccato dots should be played on the string.

Shuckin' the Corn

American Folk Song

score page 120 • student page 24

Singing songs with work themes was a popular way of completing a difficult task. Work songs contained a strong beat so that workers could synchronize their motions and work faster.

Including the piano part in performance will keep the spirit of this piece light and bouncy. Play this song confidently and drive towards the end without a *ritard*.